Homework Helpers English

Ages 9–10

Key Stage 2/Year 5

An imprint of Pearson Education

Harlow, England · London · New York · Reading, Massachusetts · San Francisco
Toronto · Don Mills, Ontario · Sydney · Tokyo · Singapore · Hong Kong · Seoul
Taipei · Cape Town · Madrid · Mexico City · Amsterdam · Munich · Paris · Milan

Series editors:
Stuart Wall & Geoff Black
With thanks to Val Mitchell for additional material and Heather Ancient for editorial development work

A complete range of **Homework Helpers** is available.

		ENGLISH	MATHS	SCIENCE
Key Stage 1	Ages 5–6 Year 1	✓	✓	Science is not included in the National Tests at Key Stage 1
	Ages 6–7 Year 2	✓	✓	
Key Stage 2	Ages 7–8 Year 3	✓	✓	✓
	Ages 8–9 Year 4	✓	✓	✓
	Ages 9–10 Year 5	✓	✓	✓
	Ages 10–11 Year 6	✓	✓	✓

Pearson Education Limited
Edinburgh Gate, Harlow
Essex CM20 2JE, England
and Associated Companies throughout the world

First published 2000

British Library Cataloguing in Publication Data
A catalogue entry for this title is available from the British Library

ISBN 0-582-38146-0

Printed in Great Britain by Henry Ling Limited, at the Dorset Press, Dorchester, DT1 1HD

Guidance and advice

Schools are now asked to set regular homework. Government guidelines for Year 5 (ages 9–10) suggest 30 minutes of homework a day. Children are also encouraged to do at least 10–20 minutes of reading.

The Literacy Hour

The daily Literacy Hour was introduced into schools in September 1999. During this session, teachers focus on three broad areas: word, sentence and text. The aim of the Literacy Hour is to develop a child's reading and writing skills.

All the activities in this book are written to complement the Literacy Hour. The emphasis is on short, enjoyable exercises designed to stimulate a child's interest in language. Each activity will take 10–20 minutes, depending on the topic, and the amount of writing and drawing.

Themes and topics

Throughout the book key words have been set in **bold** text – these highlight the themes and content of the activities, and provide a guide to the topics covered.

Encourage your child

Leave your child to do the activity on their own, but be available to answer any questions. Try using phrases like: That's a good idea! How do you think you could do it? What happens if you do it this way? These will encourage your child to think about how they could answer the question for themselves.

If your child is struggling …

Children who need help with reading or writing may need you to work with them. If your child is struggling with the writing, ask them to find the answer and then write it in for them. Remember even if your child gets stuck, be sure to tell them they are doing well.

Check the answers together

When they have done all they can, sit down with them and go through the answers together. Check they have not misunderstood any important part of the activity. If they have, try to show them why they are going wrong. Ask them to explain what they have done, right or wrong, so that you can understand how they are thinking.

You will find answers to the activities at the back of this book. You can remove the last page if you think your child might look at the answers before trying an activity. Sometimes there is no set answer because your child has been asked for their own ideas. Check that your child's answer is appropriate and shows they have understood the question.

Be positive!

If you think your child needs more help with a particular topic try to think of some similar but easier examples. You don't have to stick to the questions in the book – ask your own: Did you like that? Can you think of any more examples? Have a conversation about the activity. Be positive, giving praise for making an effort and understanding the question, not just getting the right answers. Your child should enjoy doing the activities and at the same time discover that learning is fun.

More on Spelling

Help your child to keep a list of words that they tend to spell incorrectly. Encourage your child to use these words regularly in their own writing, so as to get into the habit of spelling them correctly. Help your child break down words into separate sounds or syllables ('home-work', 'read-ing'). This makes the spelling and reading of unfamiliar words easier.

Children can test themselves in the following way:

Look at the word
Say the spelling out loud
Cover the word so they can't see it
Write it down
Check that it's spelt correctly

Poems, songs and nursery rhymes can help with a child's spellings because they encourage children to develop an awareness of sound patterns and an understanding of the link between sounds and letters.

Leave it out

Here are some phrases and sentences where some words are **contractions** and need apostrophes. However, some are already correct. If you think they're correct, put a tick. If you think they need apostrophes, write them out correctly. Two have been done for you.

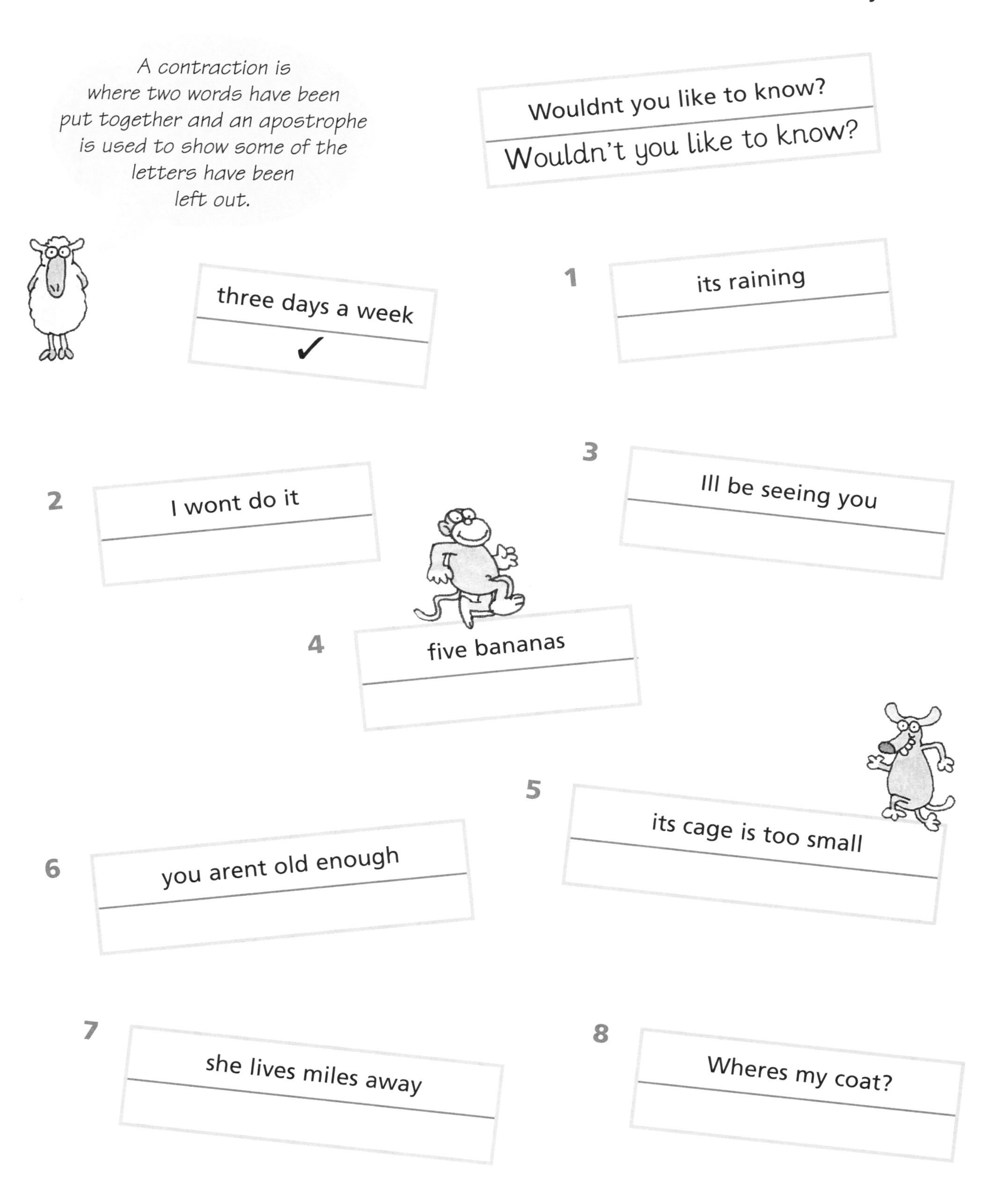

Beginning with b

It's market day and this picture shows the scene in the town square.
Look at the picture then answer the questions opposite.

Can you find ten things in the picture that begin with the letter b? Write them in the spaces below.

Now arrange the ten words you have written down in **alphabetical order**. Remember that as they all begin with b, you will have to arrange them according to the next letters in each word, beginning with the second letter.

1 ______ 6 ______

2 ______ 7 ______

3 ______ 8 ______

4 ______ 9 ______

5 ______ 10 ______

Now read this sentence out loud:

My bright blue ball bounced back to Betty.

What does it sound like?

Most of the words start with the same letter.

We call the use of the same sound at the beginning of as many words as possible ***alliteration****.*

Have a go at making up some sentences like these.

Find the rhyme

Sort these words into eight pairs of words that **rhyme**. Write each pair in one of the spaces at the bottom of the page.

This is quite tricky – sometimes different groups of letters can make the same sound!

eight

sleep

taste

soup

heart

bite

code

hoop

term

fight

cart

road

firm

heap

waist

late

Can you think of other words that rhyme but are spelt differently?

World crossword

The answers to this crossword are all countries and continents.

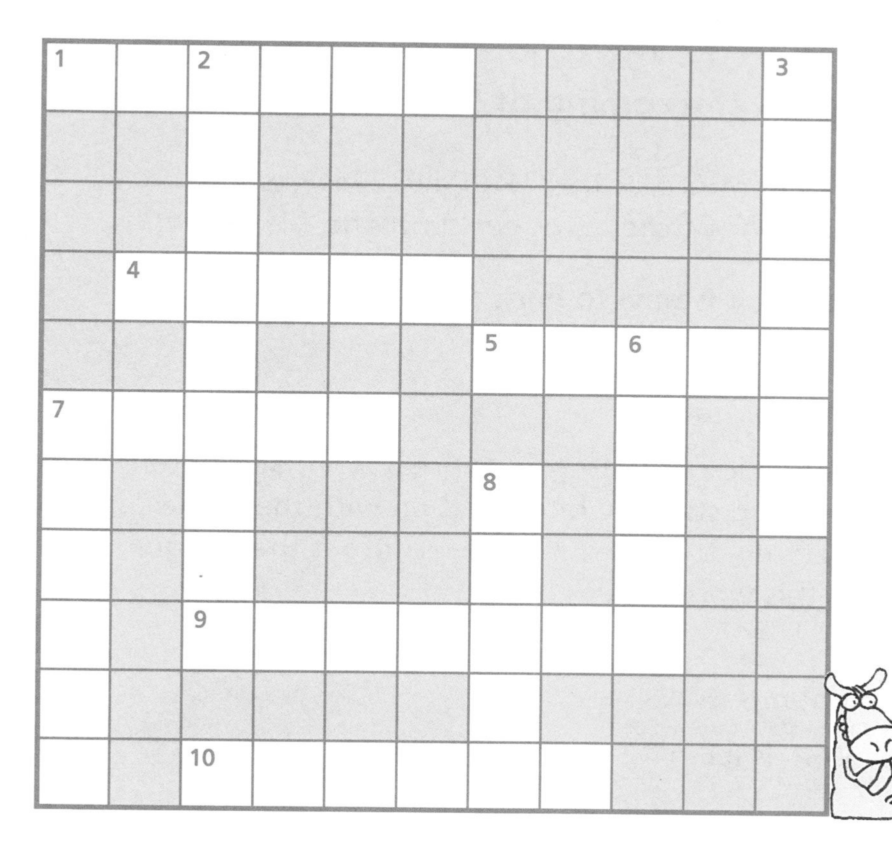

All the answers to this crossword are **proper nouns.** Think about how you will write them.

ACROSS

1. Just across the Channel. (6 letters)
4. On a map this looks like a boot. (5 letters)
5. The name of this country also means cups and saucers. (5 letters)
7. The land of bullfighting and Flamenco dancers. (5 letters)
9. This continent has a North and South. (7 letters)
10. This country has the same name as a bird. (6 letters)

DOWN

2. Down Under. (9 letters)
3. Going by its name, this country's very cold. (7 letters)
6. Where you'll find the Taj Mahal. (5 letters)
7. The people who live here have the same name as a vegetable. (6 letters)
8. The name of this South American country *sounds* cold. (5 letters)

The Jungle Book

Adapted from the book by Rudyard Kipling

Scene 1 **The coming of Shere Khan**

A cave with a small entrance. Father Wolf awakens from his daily rest. Mother Wolf watches over her cubs who are playing.

Father Wolf Augrh, it is time to hunt again.

Tabaqui
(voice from outside the cave)
Good luck go with you, O great wolf; and good luck and strong white teeth go with the noble children, that they may never forget the hungry in this world.

Mother Wolf
(protecting her young)
Who is it?

Father Wolf A jackal.

Tabaqui, the jackal, appears in the entrance of the cave.

Tabaqui Not just a jackal – it is I, Tabaqui, the Dish-Licker.

Father Wolf What do you seek, Tabaqui? You maker of mischief, you teller of tales and eater of rags.

Tabaqui It is true, Father Wolf, it is all too true. I know you despise me, and I deserve your scorn. But surely you will not refuse me the scraps of your lair?

The roar of Shere Khan is heard in the distance. Father Wolf speaks stiffly.

Father Wolf Enter then, and look for yourself. But there is no food here.

Tabaqui For a wolf, no. But for so mean a person as myself, a dry bone is a good feast. Who am I, the humble Tabaqui, the mangy Dish-Licker, to pick and choose?

Father Wolf takes a bone from a pile and throws it before Tabaqui.

Father Wolf A bone for you.

Tabaqui sniffs it and licks his lips.

Tabaqui All thanks for this good meal. Ah, how beautiful your noble children are! How large are their eyes.

Mother Wolf You must know, Tabaqui, that there is nothing so unlucky as to praise children to their faces.

Tabaqui My apologies. Have I made mischief again? Well, let me tell you some news. Shere Khan, the great tiger, has shifted his hunting grounds. He will hunt among these hills for the next moon, so he has told me.

Father Wolf looks angry.

Read the text carefully then **answer these questions**.

1 How does Tabaqui the jackal describe himself?

____

2 How does Father Wolf describe Tabaqui the jackal?

____

3 What news does Tabaqui bring to the wolf family?

____

4 Which character is heard but not seen?

____

5 Where is the scene set?

____

Dictionary quiz

Here is a page from a **dictionary.** You will need to use it to answer the questions on the opposite page.

Kk

kaleidoscope *noun* a tube fitted with mirrors and pieces of coloured glass which shows coloured patterns when turned

kangaroo *noun* (*young* **joey**) an animal which jumps along on large back legs and carries its young in a special pocket

red kangaroo with a joey in its pouch

keen *adjective* eager to do something; liking to do something; **keenly** *adverb*; **keenness** *noun*

keep *verb* **(keeps, keeping, kept)** **1** to have without giving back; **2 keep on** to do again and again; **3** to have or hold for some time; **4** to take care of; **5** to own; to have the use of; **6** to cause to continue, to stay, or to remain

kennel *noun* a small house for a dog

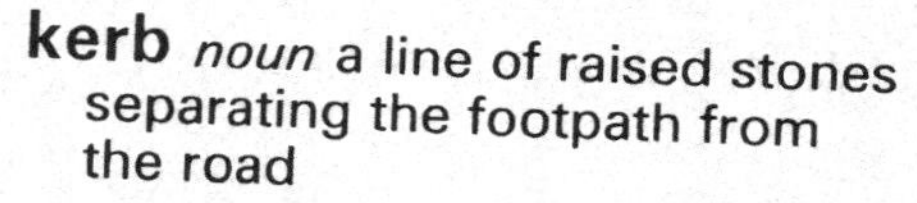

kerb *noun* a line of raised stones separating the footpath from the road

ketchup *noun* a sauce, made usually of tomatoes, for flavouring food

kettle *noun* a pot with a lid, handle, and spout for heating water to make tea, coffee, etc

key *noun* **1** a metal instrument for locking or unlocking a door, winding a clock, etc: **keyhole, key ring**; **2** a part of a piano, computer, etc, that is pressed with the finger: **keyboard**; **3** something that explains or helps you to understand, such as the list of symbols or abbreviations on a map; **4** a set of musical notes with a certain starting note

kick *verb* **1** to hit with the foot; **2** to move the feet backwards and forwards; **kick** *noun*; **kicker** *noun*

kid *noun* **1** a child or young person; **2** a young goat

kidnap *verb* to take somebody away and ask for money in return for bringing him or her back safely; **kidnapper** *noun*

kill *verb* to cause somebody or something to die; **killer** *noun*

kilogram also **kilo** *noun* a measure of weight equal to 1000 grams or 2.21 pounds

kilometre *noun* a measure of length equal to 1000 metres or 0.62 miles

[1]**kind** **(*say* kynd)** *noun* a group that are alike; type; sort

[2]**kind** *adjective* helpful; gentle and wanting to do good; **kindness** *noun*

1 What is a young kangaroo called?

2 What is ketchup usually made of?

3 What noun is used to name a person who kidnaps?

4 If the word kid is used to mean an animal, what animal does it refer to?

5 What noun comes from the word keen?

6 How many different meanings does the dictionary give for the word key?

7 What shorter word means the same as kilogram?

8 How many metres are there in a kilometre?

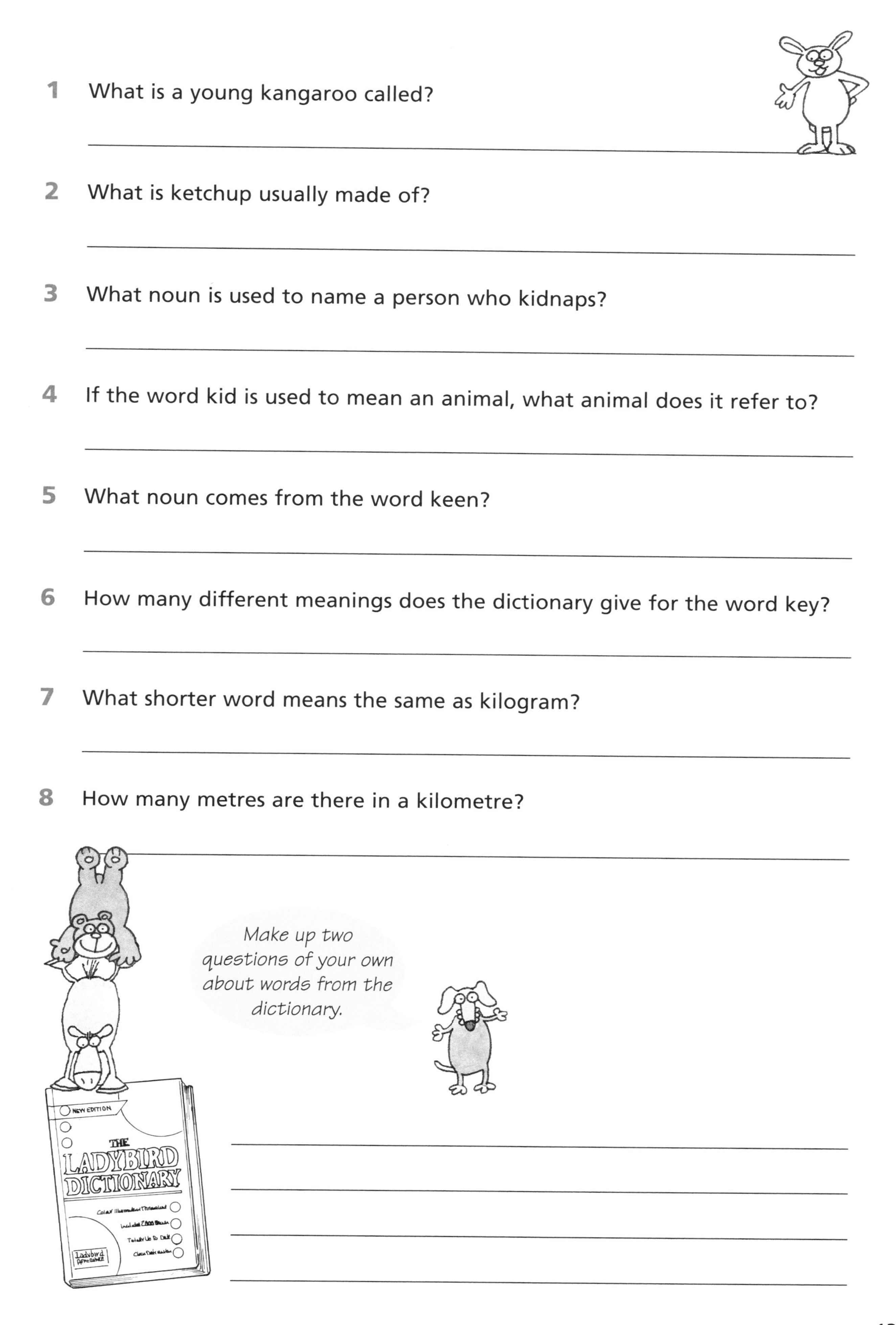

Tell me more

Here are some words you can use instead of **said**:

added demanded bellowed began pleaded revealed enquired suggested admitted apologised

Choose words from this list to put in the spaces below.

1 I thought she had finished speaking, but then she ______________ , 'So what do you think of that?'

2 A new cure for baldness has been discovered, the newspaper ______________ .

3 'Hand over the money,' the robber ______________ .

4 When he was arrested, the robber immediately ______________ he had committed the crime.

5 The teacher was furious. 'Where do you think you're going?' he ______________ at the top of his voice.

6 'It's a very long story,' she ______________ , 'but I'll tell it to you.'

7 'Please help me,' she ______________ .

8 'When's the next train to London?' the man ______________ .

9 'I'm sorry,' the man in the ticket office ______________ . 'The last train has just left.'

10 'You could try taking an overnight coach,' another passenger ______________ .

Using different words to said often gives the reader more information.

Can you think of any other alternatives to said you could have used?

Turn back the clock

The column on the left is for **present tense** verbs. The column on the right is for **past tense** verbs. Fill in the gaps.

	PRESENT	PAST
1	catch	caught
2	________	met
3	throw	________
4	________	was
5	________	ran
6	climb	________

	PRESENT	PAST
7	________	thought
8	draw	________
9	write	________
10	________	hid
11	spin	________
12	hear	________

Put these sentences into the past tense.

13 I see him by the door. ______________________________

14 I have a hole in my coat. ______________________________

15 She knows him very well. ______________________________

16 They are very excited. ______________________________

17 She lights the fire. ______________________________

Animal moves

Sort these words into ten pairs, matching each animal with the word that **describes how it might move**. One has been done for you.

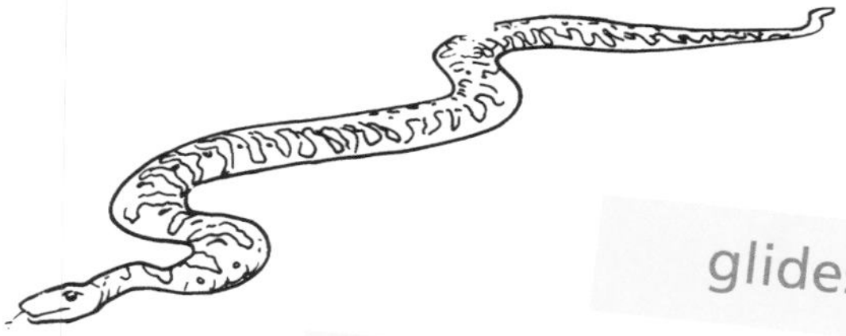

crawls

glides

swoops

eagle

jumps

snake

monkey

mouse

cock

climbs

struts

gallops

bull

tortoise

waddles

charges

horse

frog

scampers

duck

a frog jumps

Sort them out!

Arrange each of these sets of words in order. Put the **strongest word** at the top of the stairs, the **weakest word** at the bottom. Here's an example.

These words have different strengths of meaning. Boiling is much hotter than warm.

Boiling
Hot
Warm

warm, boiling, hot

1 freezing, cool, cold

2 hideous, plain, ugly

3 delicious, edible, tasty

4 bright, light, dazzling

5 discussion, row, disagreement

6 microscopic, small, minute

7 angry, outraged, displeased

8 scared, terrified, nervous

In other words

A **thesaurus** can help us when we've used the same word more than once and want to find a different word to use. It can also help us when we're looking for just the right word to describe something. Here's a page from a thesaurus, with some questions about it on the opposite page.

greasy *(a greasy hamburger)* **oily** chips, **fatty** meat

great 1 *(a great monster)* a **large** box, a **big** house, a **huge** man, an **enormous** tree, a **gigantic** spaceship, a **colossal** mountain, a **massive** amount **2** *(a great idea)* a **brilliant** game, a **sensational** present, a **cool** shirt, an **excellent** song, a **wonderful** time, a **fantastic** player, a **super** holiday **3** *(great artists)* a **first-class** scientist, a **famous** doctor, a **well-known** writer, an **important** building, a **top** actor, a **world-class** tennis player, a **leading** athlete

greedy *(Greedy Alex has finished the ice cream!)* He **eats too much**. He's a **pig**, a **greedy-guts**.

green *(green grass)* **emerald, jade, sea green, bottle green, olive, pea green**

greet *(Ms Gage greeted them on their first day at school.)* Let's **welcome** our speaker, Mr Chan. The teacher **shook hands** with my father and **introduced herself**. The soldiers **saluted** the general.

[1]**grin** *(grinning at me from the back of the bus)* The baby **smiled** at the teddy bear. Louisa **beamed** when she won her prize. Serena **smirked** and said, 'I told you so.'

[2]**grin** *(a huge grin)* a **smile**, a **beam** of delight, a **smirk**

grip *(Mrs Mott gripped her daughter's hand.)* She **held on tight** as they crossed the road. I **grasped** my bag in my left hand. I **clutched** my books under my arm. Deirdre **kept a grip on** the money. The dog **held fast** to Anna's trousers. He **clung on** even though she was running. He managed to **hang on**!

groan *(He groaned in pain.)* The boy **moaned** with cold. The door **creaked** open behind him. The class **sighed** when Ms Dixon said there was a test.

ground 1 *(on the ground)* some water on the **floor**, some **land** for building. The ball fell to **earth** somewhere by the trees. **2** *(a football ground)* the **playground**, a playing **field**, a hockey **pitch**

group *(a group of children)* a **set** of CDs, a **crowd** of fans, a **gang** of boys, an **army** of kids, a **band** of robbers, a **bunch** of flowers, a **clump** of trees, a **litter** of puppies, a **pack** of wolves, a **herd** of cows, a **flock** of birds, a **swarm** of bees, **lots** of them

shoal of fish

1 According to the thesaurus, what word can be used to describe a group of trees?

____

2 A very large tree might be described as a great tree. What word does the thesaurus suggest could be used instead of great?

____

3 According to the thesaurus, how do soldiers greet a general?

____

4 'A man has bought some ground in order to build a house on it.' What word does the thesaurus suggest you use instead of ground in this sentence?

____

5 What type of sound, similar to a groan, does a door sometimes make?

____

6 How many alternative expressions does the thesaurus give for the word green?

____

7 What name does the thesaurus give for the type of ground on which hockey is played?

____

8 Which type of grin shows the most pleasure – a smile, a beam of delight or a smirk?

____

All sorts of nouns

Find the nouns in this list of words. There are ten altogether. Decide if each noun is a **common noun**, a **proper noun** or a **collective noun** then write it in the correct column at the bottom of the page.

Nouns are naming words. Most nouns are common nouns.

Collective nouns are the names given to groups. Proper nouns are the names of particular people, places etc.

from generosity with comfortable swarm honesty late ability because regiment hyena Patricia envelope Australia heartily important rob merrily city ask

1 Common nouns	2 Proper nouns	3 Collective nouns
______	______	______
______	______	______
______	______	______
______	______	______
______	______	______
______	______	______

Silent letters

Silent letters are letters you don't hear when you say the word out loud!

Make words by adding **silent letters** to the beginning of each of the following. The first one has been done for you.

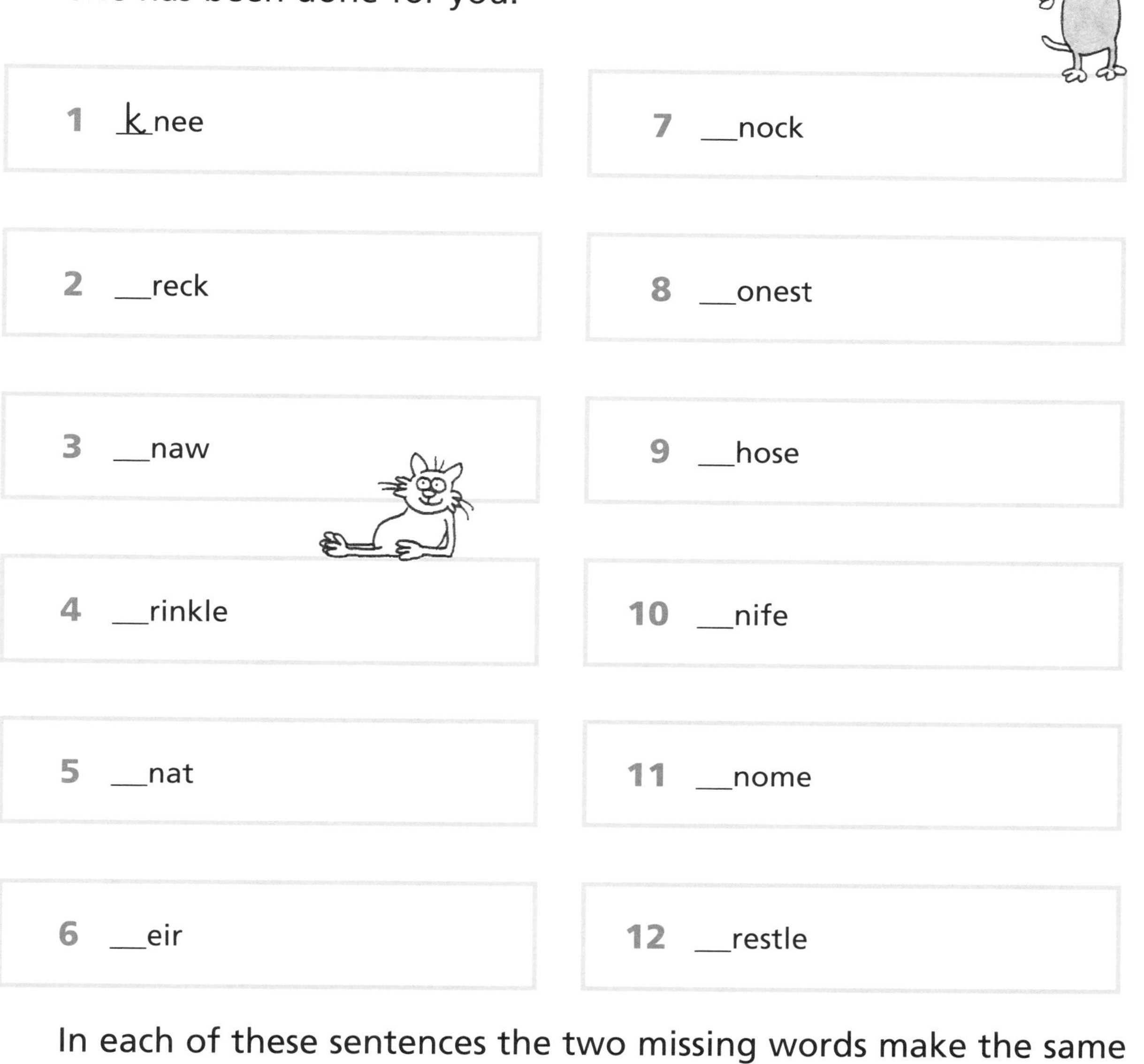

1 k nee

2 __reck

3 __naw

4 __rinkle

5 __nat

6 __eir

7 __nock

8 __onest

9 __hose

10 __nife

11 __nome

12 __restle

In each of these sentences the two missing words make the same sound but are spelt differently. One of the words has a silent letter, the other does not. Write the missing words in the spaces.

13 I've spent the __________ day digging this __________ .

14 The __________ arrived at the castle in the middle of the __________ .

15 'I stood in the pouring rain __________ your doorbell for five minutes. My clothes were __________ wet.'

16 'You're __________ ! I'll take your advice and __________ a letter of complaint to the manager of the shop.'

What does it mean?

Draw lines to join each word on the left to the correct **meaning** on the right.

	Word	Meaning
1	practise	to put off until later
2	reptile	to say or do again
3	delay	to bring to an end
4	magnet	to do something regularly or over and over again, especially in order to become better at it
5	repeat	to stop for a short time
6	pause	a cold-blooded animal, such as a snake, tortoise or crocodile, that has a body covered in scales
7	terminate	to draw towards you
8	attract	an object, such as a piece of iron, steel etc. that can draw iron towards it

Group words

Sort these words into pairs, matching the **group name** with the group that the word describes. One has been done for you.

Words which tell us the names given to groups are ***collective nouns.***

band

shoal

buffaloes

fleet

bouquet

bees

singers

ships

fish

trees

swarm

flowers

musicians

clump

herd

choir

What other collective nouns can you think of?

a bouquet of flowers.

I say

On the left are some everyday **sayings**. On the right are their meanings, but they are in the wrong order. Draw lines to join each saying to its meaning.

	Saying	Meaning
1	show a clean pair of heels	a person who's not very encouraging or enthusiastic
2	the apple of one's eye	get into trouble
3	make a clean breast of something	having nothing to do
4	a wet blanket	an achievement to be proud of
5	in the same boat	a person who is cherished or doted on
6	get into hot water	in a similar situation
7	at a loose end	escape very quickly
8	a feather in one's cap	tell the whole truth

If you don't know the answer how can you find out?

Who owns it?

How can you show that something belongs to someone? You could say 'the bag belonging to Joe' or 'the toys of the children' but most often you would just add an apostrophe and an s, like this – 'Joe's bag', 'the children's toys'. But be careful, if the word is plural and ends in s, the apostrophe comes after the s – 'the bones belonging to the dogs' becomes 'the dogs' bones'.

Write some sentences using these words as **possessives**.

A possessive is where we show something belongs to somebody.

the computer owned by Mike

the mother of Sasha

the gift for Ellena

the sweets belonging to the girls

the babies of the monkeys

the ball belonging to Jake

Remember It's means it is – not that something belongs to it.

____

____

____

____

____

____

The Owl and the

Here's a famous poem written mo
by Edward Lear. Read it then **ans**
opposite page.

Edward Lear wrote nonsense poems. They're called this because they're silly and funny.

The Ov
In a beaut
They took some honey, and plen
Wrapped up in a five-pound note.
The Owl looked up to the stars above,
And sang to a small guitar,
'O lovely Pussy! O Pussy, my love,
What a beautiful Pussy you are,
You are,
You are,
What a beautiful Pussy you are!'

Pussy said to the Owl, 'You elegant fowl!
How charmingly sweet you sing!
O let us be married! too long we have tarried
But what shall we do for a ring?'
They sailed away for a year and a day,
To the land where the Bong-tree grows,
And there in a wood a Piggy-wig stood,
With a ring at the end of his nose,
His nose,
His nose,
With a ring at the end of his nose.

'Dear Pig, are you willing to sell for one shilling
Your ring?' Said the Piggy, 'I will.'
So they took it away, and were married next day
By the Turkey who lives on the hill.
They dined on mince, and slices of quince,
Which they ate with a runcible spoon,
And hand in hand, on the edge of the sand,
They danced by the light of the moon,
The moon,
The moon,
They danced by the light of the moon.

1 How much money did the Owl and the Pussy-Cat take with them?

less than five pounds		five pounds		(tick the right answer)
more than five pounds				

2 What time of day was it when they set off?

day		night	

3 How can you tell?

____

____

4 Whose idea was it that they should get married?

the Owl's		the Pussy-Cat's		the Piggy's		the Turkey's	

5 When they danced hand in hand, where were they?

near the sea		a long way from the sea	

6 How can you tell?

____

____

7 This poem has lots of words that rhyme. Write next to each of these words the word in the poem that rhymes with it.

above		hill	
wood		moon	

Similar words

Sort these words into pairs with similar meanings. Write each pair in one of the blank spaces at the bottom of the page.

Words which have similar meanings are called ***synonyms.***

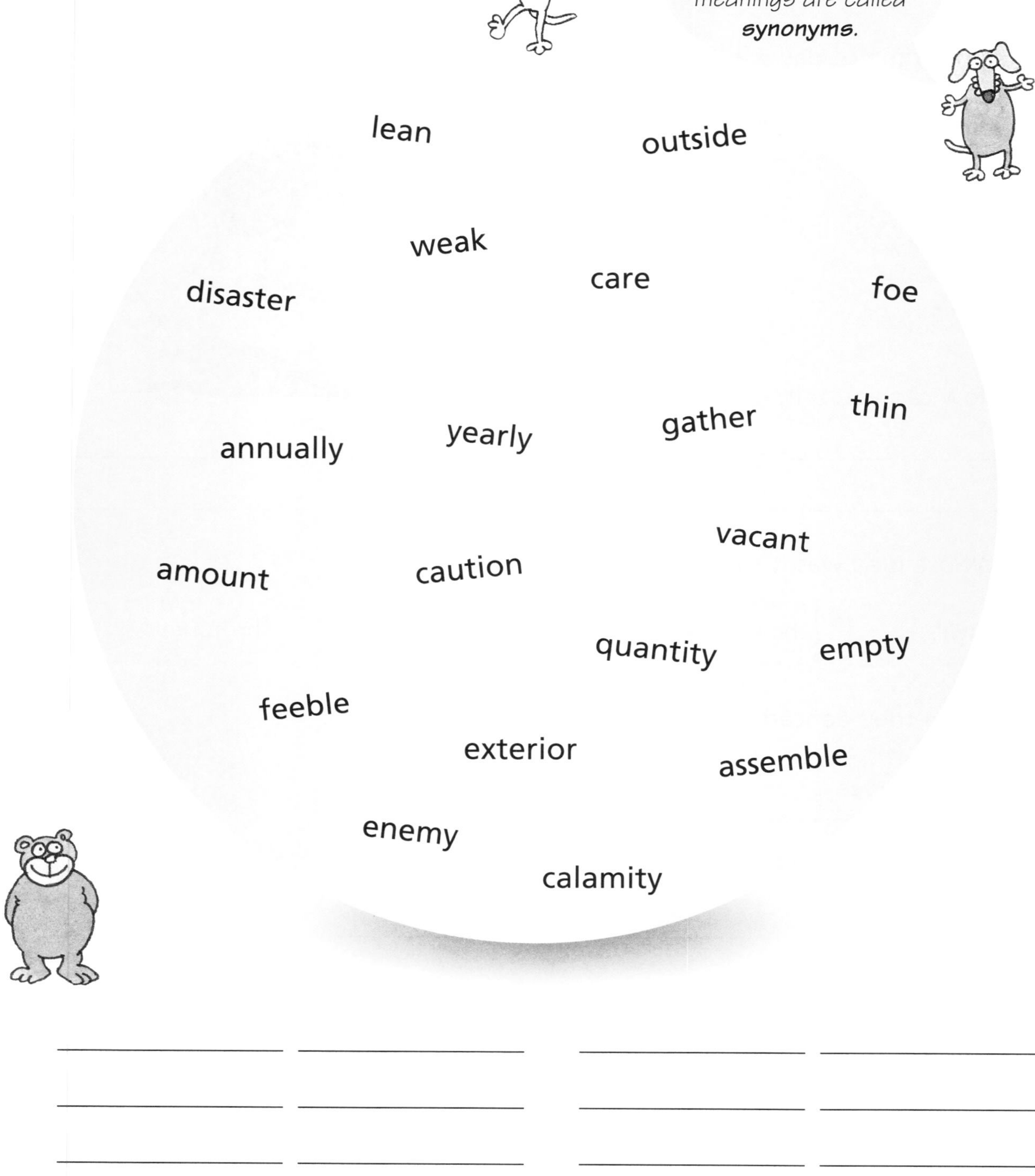

All join in

Here are ten **conjunctions**:

before	after	until
although	when	while
unless	or	because

if

Choose the conjunction from the list that fits best into each of the sentences below.

1. I try to remember to brush my teeth ____________ I go to bed.
2. My brother wanted his pudding but he had to wait ____________ the whole family had finished their first course.
3. I liked a story every night ____________ I was younger.
4. We'll go at seven o'clock ____________ you'd rather go at eight.
5. I had to choose between two presents and, ____________ I liked the book, I chose the football.
6. Dad said, 'Do you want an orange ____________ an apple?'
7. My sister made a model ____________ I read my book.
8. I could not see the film ____________ I was not old enough.
9. I found your purse on the floor just ____________ you had dropped it.
10. My hamster will be frightened ____________ you shout at it.

Adverb extra

These two pages are all about **adverbs**. First you need to find ten adverbs in the list of words below. Write them in the spaces at the bottom of the page.

Remember: an adverb describes an action.

silly anxiously

heavy pretty jelly

eventually

groan

patiently fondly

visibly

sly silently sulkily

look

clumsily

joyfully rally

say

heavily run

______________________ ______________________

______________________ ______________________

______________________ ______________________

______________________ ______________________

______________________ ______________________

Now for each of the verbs below, think of **three** suitable adverbs that might go with them. One has been done for you.

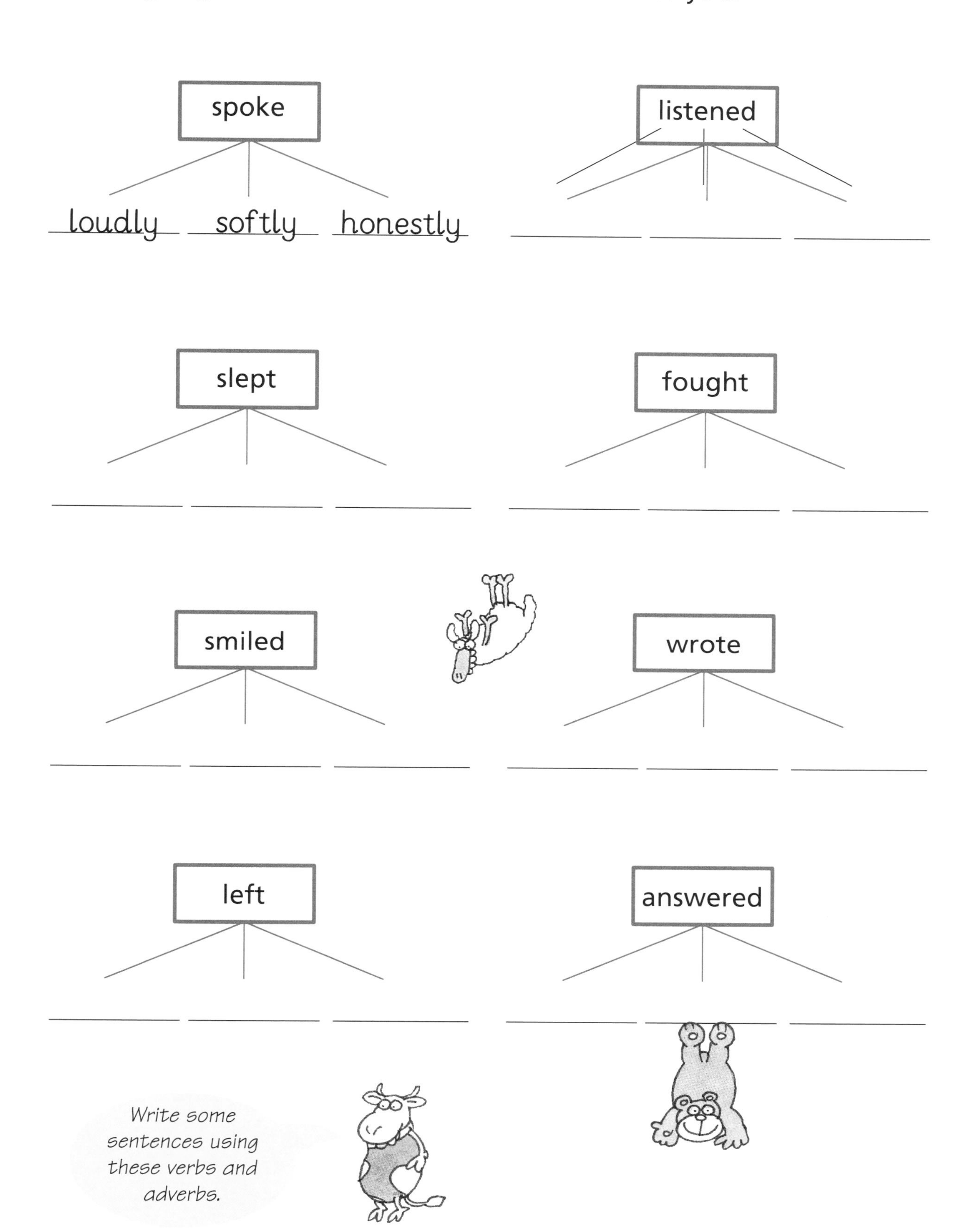

Which one is it?

Each of these sentences has two words in brackets. One word is correct, the other word is wrong. Circle the correct word.

1. I've mislaid my school shoes again and cannot remember (where/wear) I put them.
2. Sharma was looking forward to the party, as she would be able to (where/wear) her new dress.
3. Because my sister (ate/eight) earlier she said she did not want any supper.
4. I'm making a birthday card for my brother. He is (ate/eight) tomorrow.
5. My brother has a telescope and on a clear (knight/night) I like to look at the stars with him.
6. When our class visited the stately home we were shown some armour that belonged to a (knight/night) five hundred years ago.
7. Every September Mum buys me (knew/new) school shoes.
8. 'I (knew/new) you could do it,' Dad said the first time I swam without armbands.
9. I cannot decide (weather/whether) I like chocolate or strawberry ice cream best.
10. If the (weather/whether) is very bad, netball practice will be cancelled.

***Homophones** are words with the same sound but different spellings or meanings.*

Opposite pairs

Sort these words into ten pairs of **opposites**. Write each pair in one of the spaces at the bottom of the page.

Words that have opposite meanings are called ***antonyms.***

tame separate

home deny wealthy

wild plural present

unite

abroad

absent inferior

superior poor confirm

divide

singular temporary

join

permanent

_______ _______ _______ _______

_______ _______ _______ _______

_______ _______ _______ _______

_______ _______ _______ _______

_______ _______ _______ _______

Proverbs

Complete these **proverbs** by filling in the blanks.

1. A new ____________ sweeps clean.
2. When the ____________ is away the mice will play.
3. Two ____________ are better than one.
4. Let sleeping ____________ lie.
5. Great ____________ think alike.
6. Don't count your ____________ before they are hatched.
7. Make ____________ while the sun shines.
8. More ____________, less speed.
9. An ____________ a day keeps the doctor away.
10. Don't put all your eggs in one ____________ .

What do you think these proverbs mean?

If you don't know these sayings ask an adult to help you.

Definitions

Draw lines to join each word on the right to the correct **meaning** on the left.

	Word	Meaning
1	pattern	programs which control the way a computer works
2	frost	a drawing that explains something or shows how its parts are arranged
3	monk	a small machine that sends information from one computer to another one through a phone line
4	diagram	a pointed stick of ice formed when running water freezes
5	modem	a regularly repeated arrangement of shapes and colours
6	icicle	one of a group of men who live together and have given their lives to the service of a religion
7	software	a person trained for various religious duties
8	priest	white powdery ice that forms on outside surfaces when the weather is very cold

In other words

Here is another page from a **thesaurus**, with some questions.

Rr

[1]**race** **1** *(a swimming race)* a **knockout**, a **competition**, a **championship**, a **tournament**, a **challenge**, a **contest** **2** *(people of various races)* Poodles and collies are different **breeds** of dog.

[2]**race** *(He raced downstairs.)* **rushing** out of the door, **dashing** down the steps, **running** along the path, **hurrying** along, **speeding** down the road, **sprinting** past

[1]**racket** *(a tennis racket)*

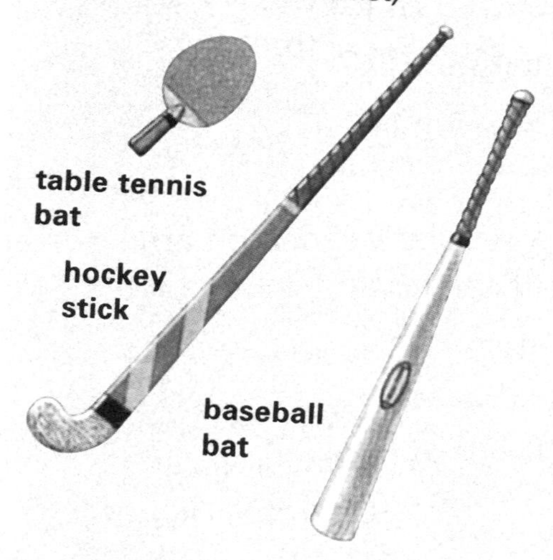

[2]**racket** *(a terrible racket)* What a **noise**! What a **commotion**! What a **din**!

rag **1** *(a floor rag)* a **cloth** for wiping the table, a **tea towel**, a **duster** **2** *(a tramp wearing nothing but rags)* in **tatters**

[1]**rain** *(heavy rain)* a **downpour**, a bad **rainstorm**, a **cloudburst**, a **shower**, a thin **drizzle**

[2]**rain** *(It's raining.)* It's **pouring**, **pouring with rain, raining cats and dogs, coming down in buckets**. It's **tipping down**. It's only **dripping, drizzling, spitting**.

raincoat *(a new raincoat)* a **mac**, a **mackintosh, waterproof jacket, anorak, parka**, a **waterproof, oilskins**

raise **1** *(Please raise your hands.)* Katy **put up** her hand first. Michael **lifted** the box. I can **pick up** two boxes that big! I can even **carry** my big sister. She **heaved** a case **up** the stairs. The crane **hoisted** the container into the air. He had to **jack up** the car to change the wheel. **2** *(to raise the prices of computer games)* They **put** them **up** on Monday. All the shops have **increased** their prices. **3** *(She raised the topic of school buses.)* Don't **mention** anything about Granny's birthday. He **brought up** the subject of pets. I **introduced** the question of higher pocket money. **4** *(raising money)* Dad's **collecting** for Oxfam. We should **bring in** some money with our Christmas concert.

rare *(a rare stamp)* an **unusual** car, a **unique** opportunity, fruit that is **scarce** at this time of year, **uncommon**, an **extraordinary** heatwave. People like her are **few and far between**.

rash *(a rash decision)* a **risky** business, a **reckless** journey, a **thoughtless** act, **irresponsible** behaviour, **careless** driving, **not taking** enough **care**

rather *(rather small)* **quite** big, a **bit** slow, **slightly** warmer, **fairly** good, **pretty** easy

1 What word could you use instead of the word raised in the sentence 'The crane raised the container into the air'?

____

2 What type of rag would you use to wipe a table?

____

3 Three words for rain are a rainstorm, a shower and drizzle. Write them in order, putting the weakest word first and the strongest last.

____

4 A mackintosh is a type of raincoat. What word is a shortened version of the word mackintosh?

____

5 A racket is used to play tennis. What is used to play hockey?

____

6 What single word could replace the expression 'raising money' in the sentence 'I'm raising money for Oxfam'?

____

7 The people of the world belong to different races. What word similar in meaning to races is used to refer to different types of dogs?

____

8 Explain how the sentence 'What a racket!' could have two very different meanings.

____

Double trouble

The answer to the clue on the left and the clue on the right is the same word! Write your answers inside the brackets. The first one has been done for you.

	CLUE	ANSWER	CLUE
1	step on a ladder	(rung)	the doorbell has done this
2	a piece of computer equipment	(________)	a little furry creature
3	travels along tracks	(________)	could be part of a wedding dress
4	blonde	(________)	right and just
5	a container	(________)	to fight with your fists
6	holds up a fence	(________)	mail
7	punishment payment	(________)	of good quality
8	part of the eye	(________)	someone who goes to school
9	expensive	(________)	affectionate name for someone
10	seed	(________)	lines in wood

Words that are spelt the same and sound the same but have different meanings are called ***homonyms.***

Alphabet soup

Using only the letters in this alphabet soup, find the answers to the clues. You can use the same letters more than once.

	CLUE	ANSWER
1	These fall from trees in the autumn	_ _ _ _ _ _
2	If you've got some climbing to do, this might help	_ _ _ _ _ _
3	A person who is owned by another person and has to work for them	_ _ _ _ _
4	If a man does this he won't have a beard	_ _ _ _ _
5	A spot that isn't sunny might be described as this	_ _ _ _ _
6	One of these will stop your dog running away	_ _ _ _
7	Put something between two slices of this and you'll have a sandwich	_ _ _ _ _

What does it mean?

Study this page from a **dictionary**, and then answer the questions.

digger *noun* somebody or something that digs; a tool or machine for digging the earth

digit *noun* **1** any number from nought to nine; **2** a finger or toe; **digital** *adjective*

dining room *noun* a room in which you eat meals

dinner *noun* a main meal, eaten either at midday or in the evening

dinosaur *noun* any of several types of reptiles, some very large, that lived millions of years ago

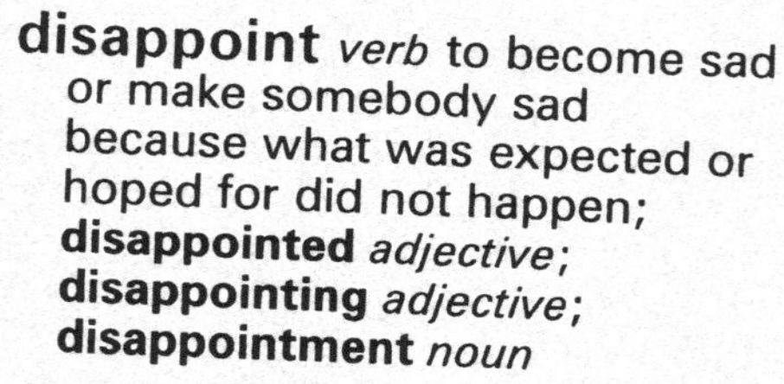

disappoint *verb* to become sad or make somebody sad because what was expected or hoped for did not happen; **disappointed** *adjective*; **disappointing** *adjective*; **disappointment** *noun*

disapprove *verb* to have a bad opinion of somebody or something; **disapproval** *noun*

disarm *verb* to give up or reduce the number of weapons or soldiers that you have

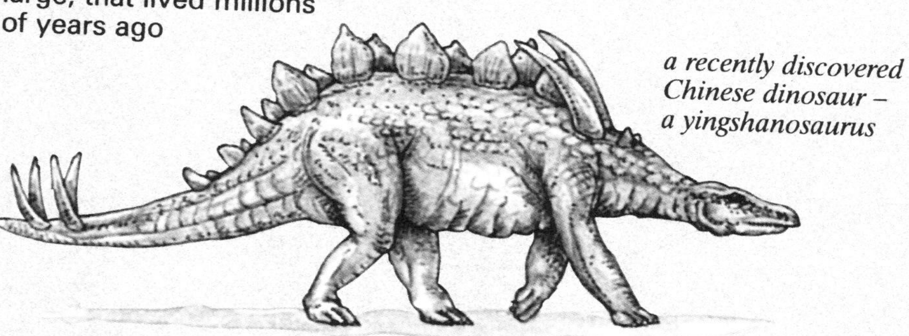

a recently discovered Chinese dinosaur – a yingshanosaurus

[1]**direct** *verb* **1** to tell somebody the way; **2** to control or manage; **director** *noun*

[2]**direct** *adjective* straight towards or straight after or behind; **directly** *adverb*

direction *noun* **1** the course or way in which a person or thing moves; **2 directions** information that tells you where to go or what to do

dirt *noun* soil, mud, dust, or anything that is not clean

dirty *adjective* **1** covered with dirt; **2** making you, or your clothes, unclean; **dirtily** *adverb*; **dirtiness** *noun*

disagree *verb* not to agree; **disagreement** *noun*

disappear *verb* to go out of sight; **disappearance** *noun*

disc *noun* **1** round flat thing; **2** a flat piece of plastic on which music or electronic information is stored

disciple *noun* somebody who is faithful to or follows a leader

discipline *noun* good behaviour and the obeying of rules; the training of somebody to behave in this way

disco *noun* a place where people dance to pop music

discover *verb* to find out or find something, especially for the first time; **discoverer** *noun*; **discovery** *noun*

disease *noun* an illness; **diseased** *adjective*

dish *noun* **1** a large, flat, and often round plate on which your food is served; **2** prepared food of one kind

1 Is the noun digger used to refer to a person, a machine or both?

____

2 If you disapprove of somebody, what noun would describe the feelings that you have?

____

3 How many digits does the number 365 have?

____

4 In what country did the yingshanosaurus dinosaur live?

____

5 What noun comes from the verb direct?

____

6 According to the dictionary, what shape does a dish often have?

____

7 What is a compact disc made of?

____

8 Would you be more likely to ask somebody for direction or directions?

____

Use the information from the dictionary to make up some questions of your own.

Haiku and cinquains

A haiku is a special sort of Japanese poem.

The poem has three lines and seventeen **syllables** arranged in the pattern

	Autumn
5 syllables	Yellow, red and brown
7 syllables	The leaves flutter to the ground
5 syllables	Birds eat ripe berries.

Now try to write a haiku for each season.

Spring

____

____

____

Summer

____

____

____

Autumn

____

____

____

Winter

____

____

____

A cinquain

This is another way of writing a poem using syllables.

Line 1 2 syllables
LIne 2 4 syllables
Line 3 6 syllables
Line 4 8 syllables
Line 5 2 syllables

The Mouse Trap

Oh no!
There is a mouse,
With shining, frightened eyes,
Heading for Granny's awful trap,
Oh no!

Oh good!
That wretched mouse
That's eaten all my sweets,
Is quite dead, there in the mouse trap.
Oh good!

Now try to write two cinquains of your own.

Try writing about the same incident from two different points of view.

Fire!

Here is a **newspaper report** of a fire.

FRIMTON ECHO

FIRE RAGES THROUGH HIGH STREET

Much of Frimton High Street was destroyed by fire yesterday when a blaze in a restaurant spread to adjoining shops. Firefighters fought to control the inferno for more than 16 hours and were still at the scene today. Miraculously, no one was injured but many shops were damaged by the flames.

The fire was first reported by paperboy Christopher Coughlan, who spotted flames coming from an upstairs window of the restaurant at 7 a.m. 'I telephoned the fire brigade and within minutes the whole restaurant was ablaze,' he said.

The fire rapidly spread. As many as seven shops are believed to have been completely destroyed, while another six have suffered damage. Marion Murphy, who runs the Frimton Art Shop, spoke for many when she said, 'It will take months or even years to recover from this. Fortunately I'm insured but I'll have to start again completely from scratch.'

The High Street was closed to traffic all day as crowds gathered at one end of the street to watch the firefighters battling the flames.

John Murphy, Chief Fire Officer, said the High Street was likely to remain closed for several more days. He also hailed paperboy Christopher Coughlan as a hero. 'Because of Christopher's call we were able to wake up people living above the shops and evacuate the buildings.'

CONTINUED ON PAGE 3

1 Write down two words from the first paragraph of the report that mean the same as fire. ______________________________

2 The word adjoining means:

next to		opposite	
nearby		similar	

(tick the right answer)

3 How many shops altogether were destroyed or damaged? ________

4 Which of the following statements is correct?

When Christopher rang the fire brigade the whole restaurant was on fire.	
Soon after Christopher rang the fire brigade the whole restaurant was on fire.	
Christopher's telephone call saved the restaurant from complete destruction.	
Christopher telephoned the fire brigade because the ground floor of the restaurant was on fire.	

5 According to the report,

Marion Murphy spoke for the whole community of Frimton	
Marion Murphy suffered more than other shopkeepers	
Marion Murphy was luckier than most other shopkeepers	
several other shopkeepers are in a similar situation to Marion Murphy	

6 The word evacuate means:

the buildings were saved		property was removed from the building	
people were made to leave the buildings		buildings were cordoned off	

What's missing?

In each of these pairs of phrases and sentences, the missing words sound the same but are spelt differently. Write the missing words in the spaces.

1 A ________ of cake.

________ and quiet.

2 A ________ of shoes.

A partridge in a ________ tree.

3 When you talk to yourself you are thinking ________ .

At the weekend I am ________ to stay up later.

4 Goldilocks had golden ________ .

It was too big to be a rabbit; it was a ________ .

5 Another word for a story is a ________ .

The horse swished its ________ to swat the flies away.

6 Lucy is Mr Snell's daughter and her brother Simon is his ________ .

The ________ shone all day when we went to the seaside.

7 I had to agree that it was ________ that my older sister received more pocket money than me.

When we catch the bus, we have to pay our ________.

8 You should be able to tell ________ from wrong by now.

My mum always encouraged me to ________ thank you letters.

Words that sound the same but have different spellings or meanings are called ***homophones.***

Preposition puzzlers

Here are some **prepositions**:

beside	on	through
over	between	
behind	across	under

Prepositions usually tell us where something is in relation to something else.

1 If you want to travel to Britain from America you have to fly ____________ the Atlantic Ocean.

2 I was sitting on the park bench when David sat down ____________ me.

3 Sarah was at the front of the queue and I was just ____________ her.

4 The magpie hovered in the air for a moment then landed ____________ our picnic table.

5 We walked ____________ the jungle for three days before we were rescued.

6 When Mum took the photograph, Tim stood in the middle, ____________ his two sisters.

7 The river flows ____________ twelve bridges before it reaches the sea.

8 He looked both ways then walked ____________ the road.

Punctuation quiz

Test your knowledge of **punctuation marks** by matching the clues and explanations on the right with the punctuation marks on the left. Draw lines to connect them together.

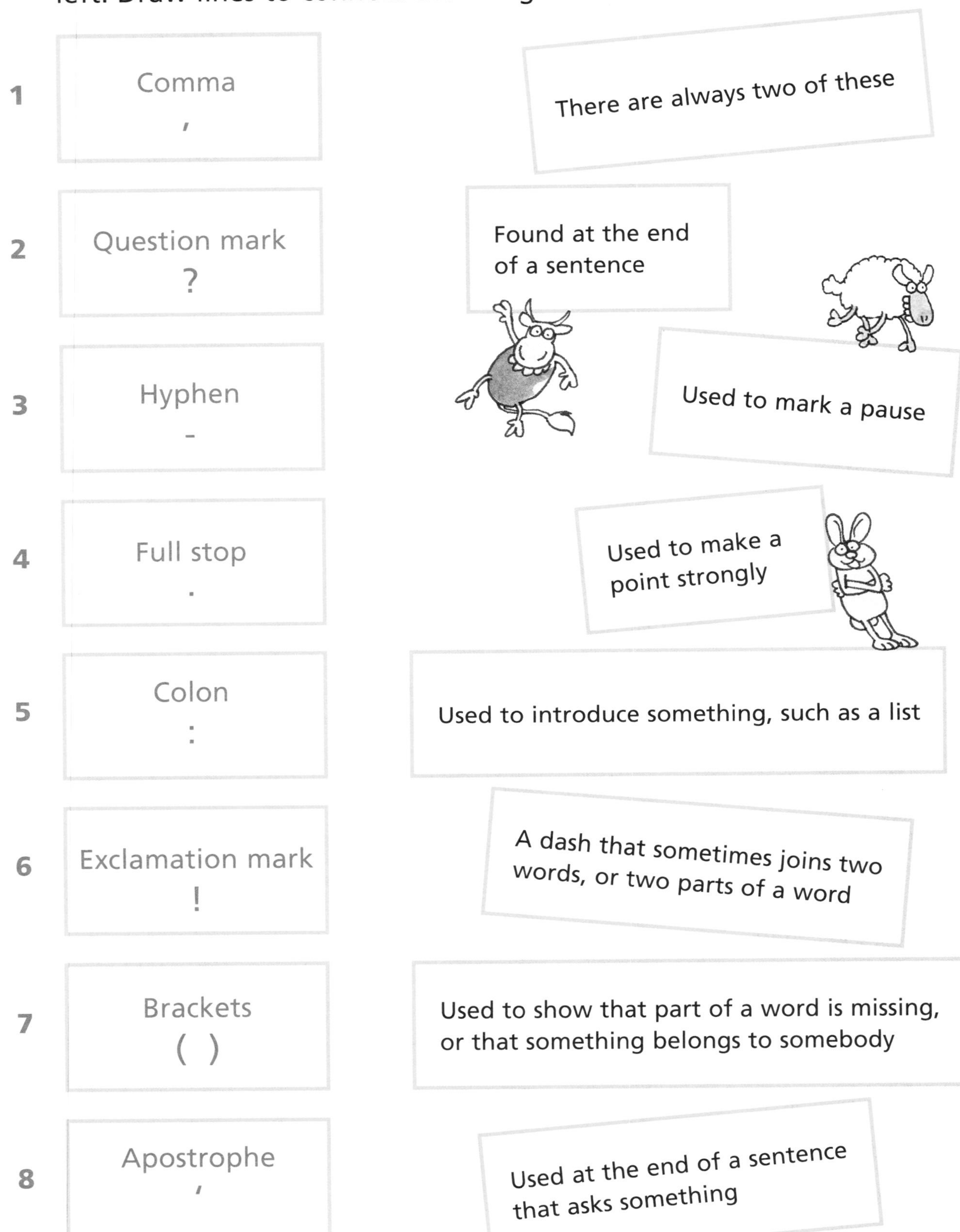

1. Comma ,
2. Question mark ?
3. Hyphen -
4. Full stop .
5. Colon :
6. Exclamation mark !
7. Brackets ( )
8. Apostrophe '

- There are always two of these
- Found at the end of a sentence
- Used to mark a pause
- Used to make a point strongly
- Used to introduce something, such as a list
- A dash that sometimes joins two words, or two parts of a word
- Used to show that part of a word is missing, or that something belongs to somebody
- Used at the end of a sentence that asks something

Spot the mistake

Here's a page from a little girl's diary. The page has ten **spelling** mistakes. Write the correct spelling of the words in the spaces at the bottom of the page.

Put a circle round the spelling mistakes.

Today I went with Mum and Dad to visit Aunt Sally. Sally is Mum's sisster. Sally's new boyfriend Pete was there. He says things like, 'I like children but I couldn't eat a hole one.' (Ha ha)

Sally has a new white sofa. I thought it looked lovly. Mum said, 'It's very lite, Sall, do you think it's practical?' She nodded at me wile she said it. I could not understand what Mum ment becuase I think I'm very practical.

After tea Dad bought some ice creams. Judy, Sally's dog, ran in from the garden and sudenly jumped up at Dad, makeing him stumble. He recovered, but a scoop of chocolate ice cream flew away from one of the cornets. Pete dived on to the sofa just in time and cort the ice cream in his hands. 'Great catch!' I shouted. Pete laughed as he let Judy lick the ice cream from his hands.

______________	______________
______________	______________
______________	______________
______________	______________
______________	______________

Get rid of got!

Usually when we write a sentence we can avoid using the word **got** by using other, better words. In each of the following sentences try to replace the words in **bold print** with a single word that sounds better. One has been done for you.

		ANSWER
1	I **got** here yesterday.	arrived
2	I **got** ten cards on my birthday.	______
3	I **got to** the station just in time.	______
4	I **got** a cold from my sister.	______
5	We **got** a lot of food at the supermarket.	______
6	I **got** to bed at nine o'clock.	______
7	He has **got** twenty goals this season.	______
8	She **got** to the top of the mountain in three hours.	______
9	I **have got** to see Mr Fisher.	______
10	She **has got** one brother and two sisters.	______

Making words

Make **nouns** from these verbs.
One has been done for you.

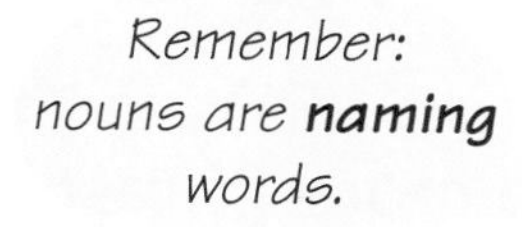

	Verb	Noun
1	Please	Pleasure
2	Think	
3	Encourage	
4	Advertise	
5	Act	
6	Move	
7	Oppose	
8	Explain	

Now make **adjectives** from these nouns.
The first has been done for you.

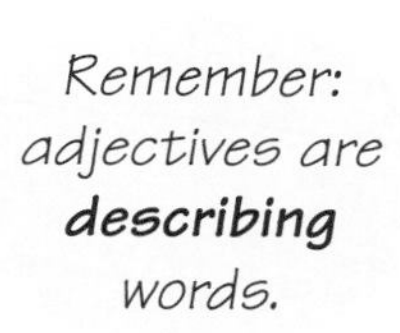

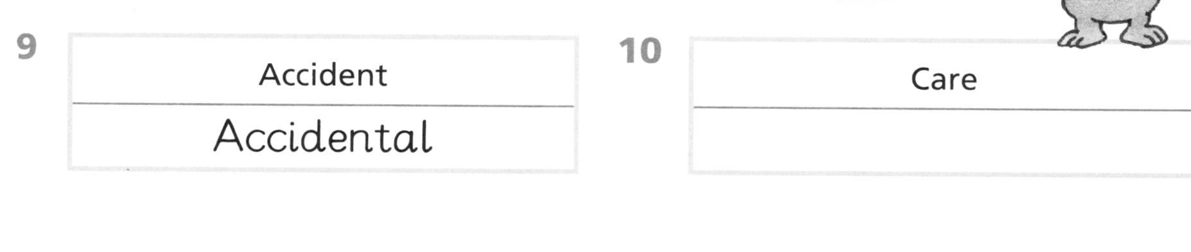

	Noun	Adjective
9	Accident	Accidental
10	Care	
11	Fool	
12	Beauty	
13	Patience	
14	Strength	
15	Anxiety	
16	Comfort	

Apostrophe catastrophe

Here are some more phrases and sentences for you to look at. Some need **apostrophes** and some do not. If you think they need apostrophes, write them out correctly.

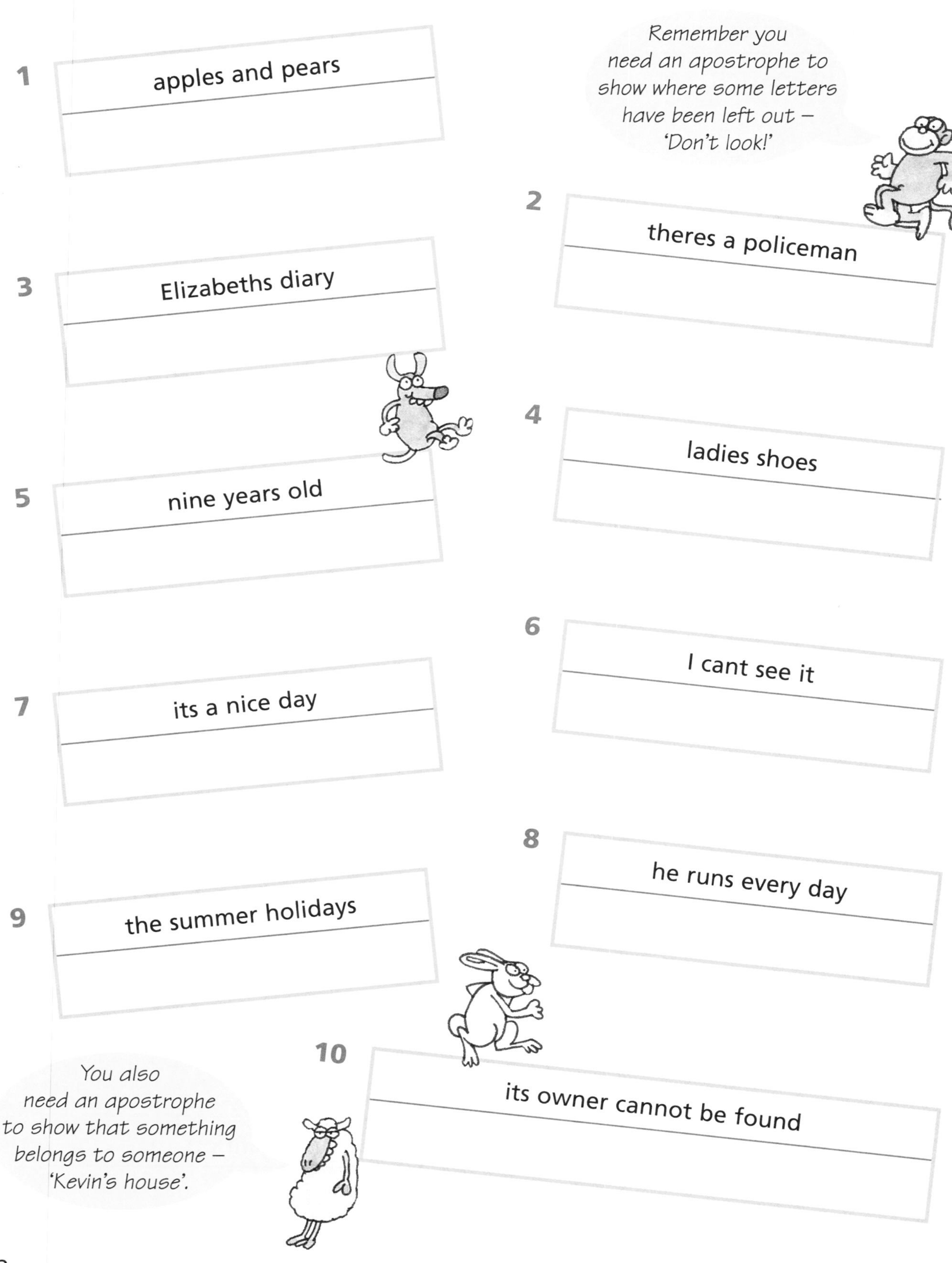

Your choice

Each of these sentences has two words in brackets. One word is correct, the other word is wrong. Circle the correct word.

1 The bus (is/are) late.

2 I (see/saw) him yesterday.

3 (Has/Have) you heard the news?

4 The police (was/were) called to the accident.

5 There (is/are) a need for more playgrounds.

6 I (am/was) not very happy when I saw what he had done.

7 The weather (was/were) very wet and windy.

8 (Wasn't/Weren't) you pleased when you heard we were coming?

9 My budgerigars Joey and Daisy (is/are) a happy couple.

10 The library (has/have) some wonderful books.

How many people or things are doing the action?

Is the sentence talking about the present or the past?

How do I do it?

The careful and well-thought-out **instructions** for making that renowned beverage, a cup of tea.

- The container which you require to hold the water needs to be clean and leak-proof, such as a kettle or saucepan.
- This container then needs to be filled from the kitchen tap with clean, clear, fresh water, which is cold to the touch.
- Place the container on some form of heating appliance such as a gas hob or an electric plate, or even an outdoor fire, providing there is a stable grid to support its weight.
- You then need to wait while the water is heated, until eventually the water reaches 100 degrees Celsius, otherwise known as boiling point. At this temperature the water will be bubbling and steam will escape from the container.
- While you are waiting for the water to heat, fetch the teapot. A china teapot is preferred because this makes the best cup of tea. Arrange the cups and saucers ready for your guests. Some people require milk and sugar with their tea so gather these at the same time.
- When the water in the container has reached the required temperature, it is necessary to warm the china teapot. A little of the steaming water needs to be poured into the teapot and swirled around to make the outside of the teapot warm to the touch.
- The crisp fresh tea leaves need then to be added to the warmed teapot. The required amount is one teaspoonful for each person partaking of tea and "one for the pot", so to speak.
- The water in the kettle needs to be brought again to boiling point and then sufficient water should be added to the pot.
- The tea must then be left for a few minutes to fully develop a satisfactory colour and flavour before it can be served. Always remember to put the milk in the cup before the tea. Add one or two teaspoonfuls of sugar, as desired.

Instructions should be clear and to the point.

Simplify these instructions to make them brief and easily understood.

The verb is often put at the start of the sentence to emphasise the action.

The first instruction has been done for you.

Only include information that is absolutely necessary.

How to make a cup of tea.

1 Fill a kettle or saucepan with cold water.

Give us a clue

The answers to these picture clues are all words that begin with the letter h. Write the answers in the spaces beneath the pictures.

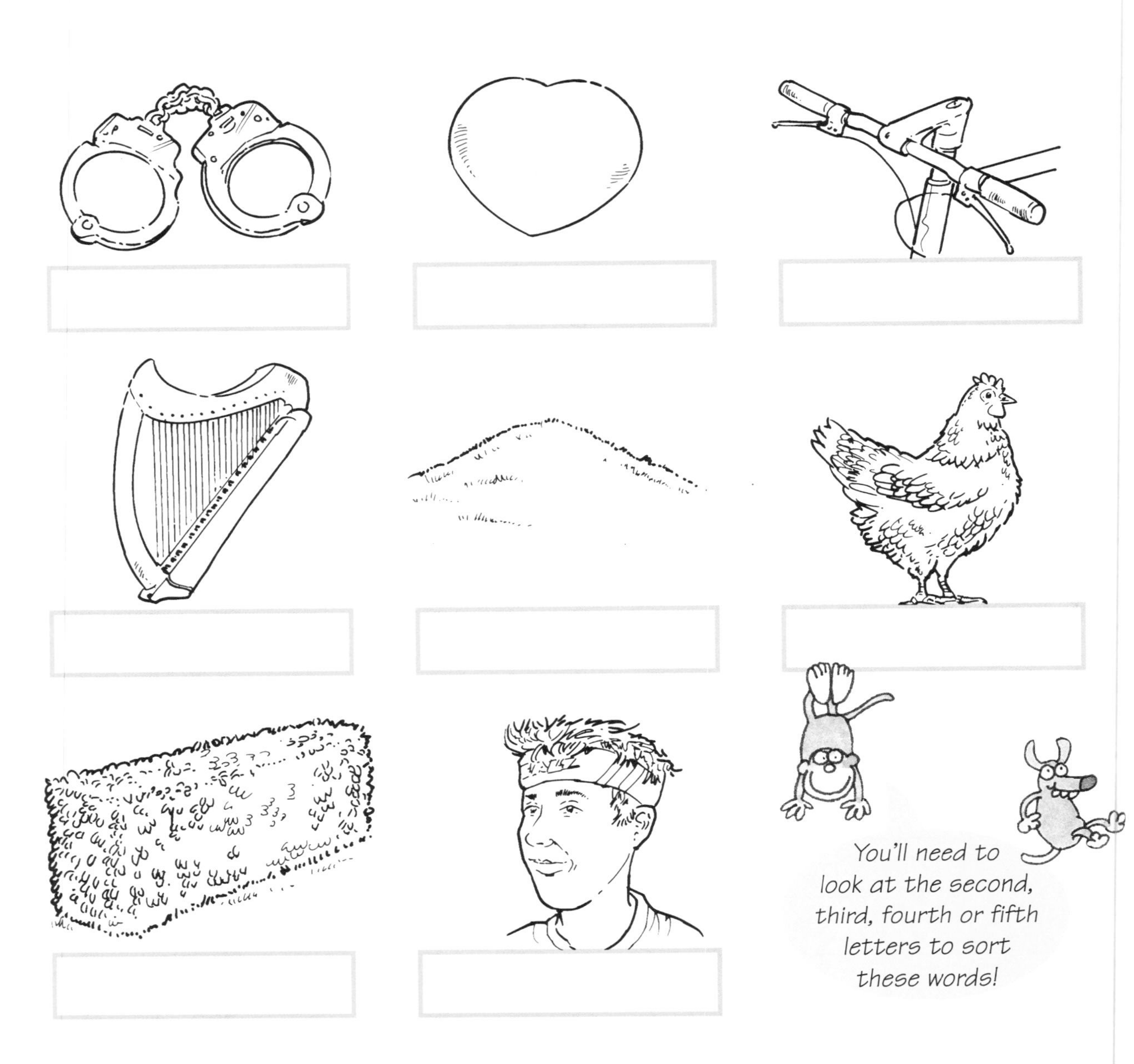

Now write the answers out again, this time arranging them in **alphabetical order**.

1 ______________________ 5 ______________________

2 ______________________ 6 ______________________

3 ______________________ 7 ______________________

4 ______________________ 8 ______________________

Check it out

Put a ring around the spelling mistakes.

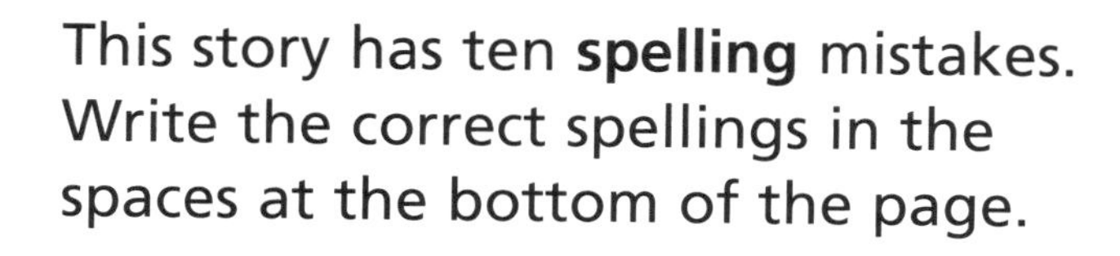

This story has ten **spelling** mistakes. Write the correct spellings in the spaces at the bottom of the page.

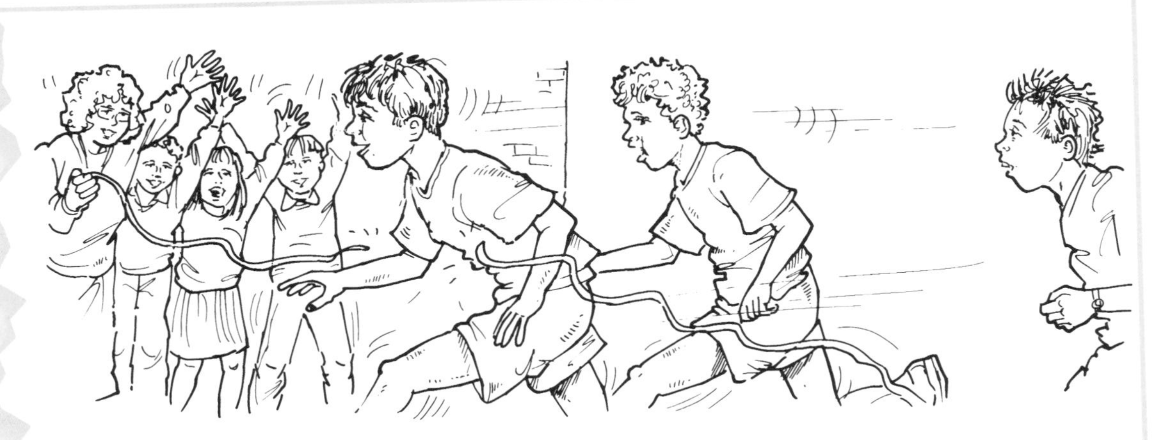

Sam shivvered as he lined up with half his class for the long disstance race. It was to be five laps around the pleyground. Sam did not enjoy sports and he had been dreding this race. Mrs Davies, the sports teacher, said, 'Don't forget, children – pace yourselves.'

Jack, the football game captane, said, 'That means run realy fast.' The others nodded in agreement. Sam was about to proetest that it did not mean that at all, when Mrs Davies shoutted, 'On your marks!' and they were off.

By the end of lap three Sam was last. But by the end of lap four he had past all but one of the exhausted runners. Now Sam ran as fast as he could and just before the finishing line ran past a red-faced, gasping Jack. Mrs Davies and the rest of his class were cheering him on as he ran threw the tape.

______________	______________
______________	______________
______________	______________
______________	______________
______________	______________

Power surge

Give these words more power by replacing them with **stronger** ones. Write your answers in the empty boxes.

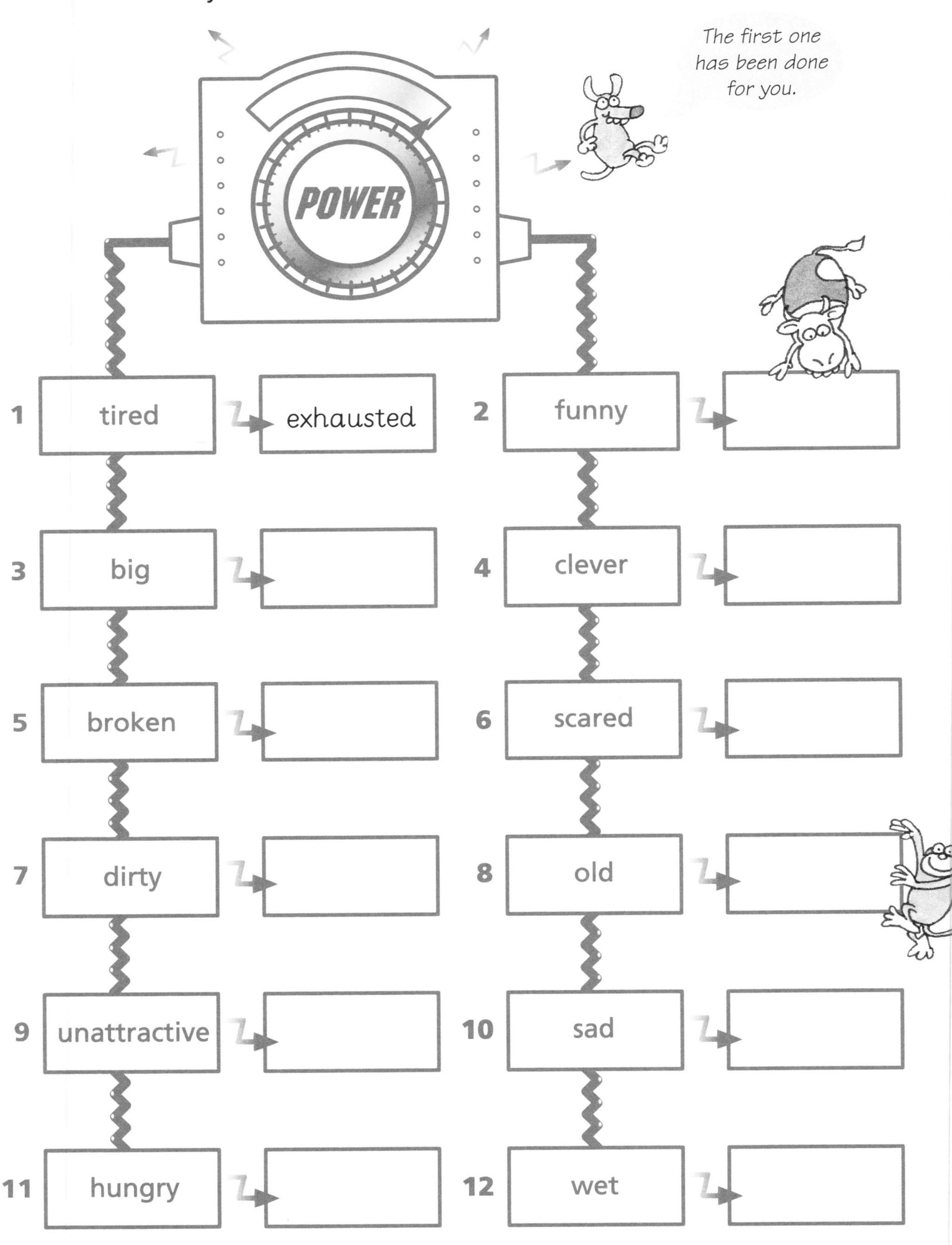

Try another word!

There are many words instead of **said** that we can use when writing. Think of a single word that could be used to describe each of the following ways of saying things. One has been done for you.

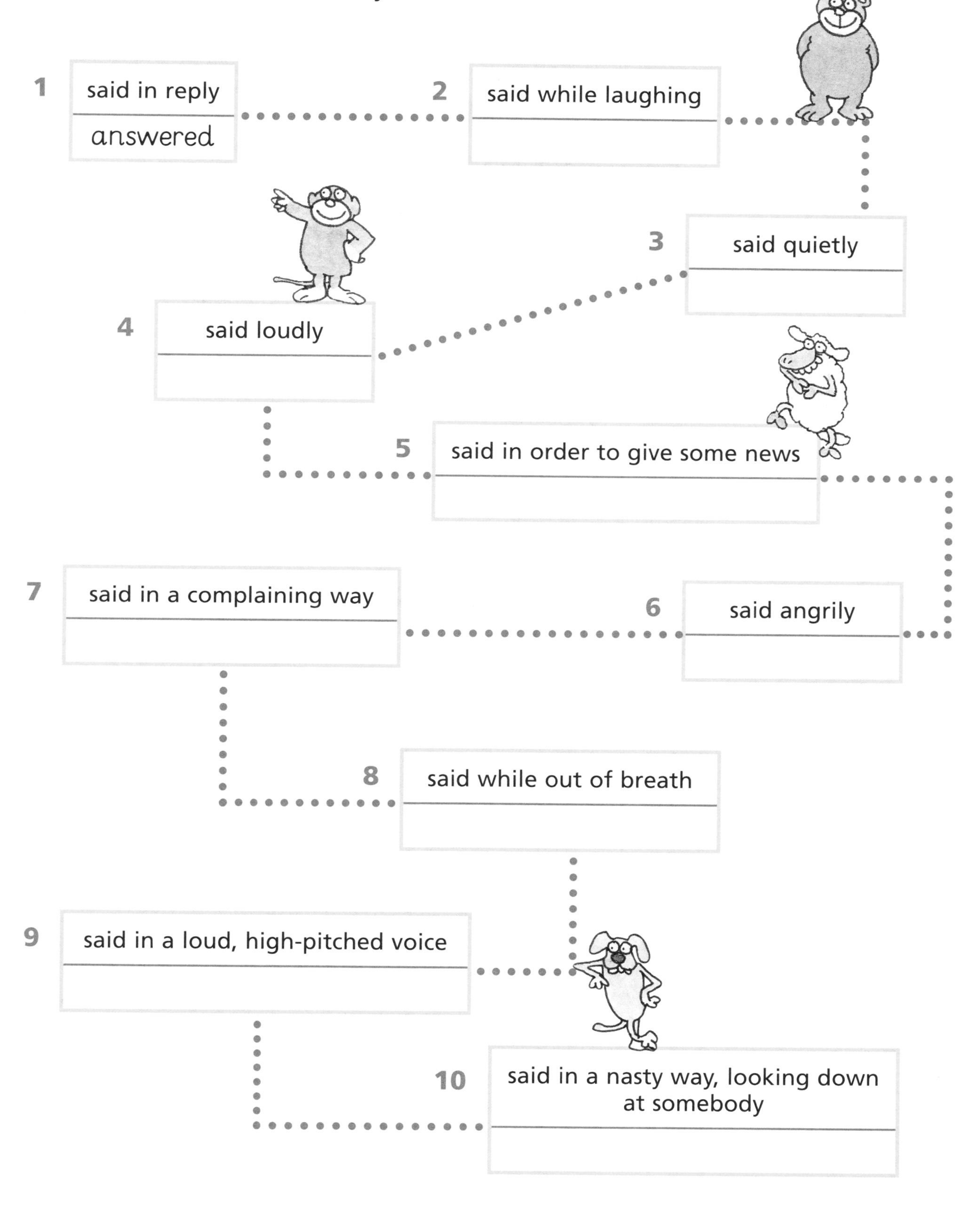

Golden sands

Here is a page from a holiday brochure. Read it then **answer the questions** on the opposite page.

GOLDEN SANDS

Holiday Park

Read this page to find out about our tremendous children's facilities...

FREE CHILDREN'S CLUBS

Our terrific Children's Clubs are every child's (and parent's) dream. Children are looked after by friendly, experienced Club Leaders and Club rooms are full of toys, books and games. When your family arrive at the Golden Sands Holiday Park, all children aged 15 and under in your party will receive a free Fun Pack and a Season Ticket giving them free admission throughout your holiday to the Club for their age group.

LITTLUNS
Ages 3–5

Organised activities in the Littluns Club include face painting, teddy bears' picnics, butterfly hunts, video sessions, ice cream treats and bedtime stories. Club activities take place for one and a half hours every day for six days and for two hours on three evenings a week.

MIDDLUNS
Ages 6–10

The Middluns Club offers mini Olympics, wacky races, fancy dress, face painting, video sessions, treasure hunts and postcard designing. Club activities take place for two hours every day for six days and for two hours on three evenings a week.

BIGUNS
Ages 11–15

The Biguns Club features talent shows, discos, beach volleyball games and video sessions. Club activities take place for two hours every day for six days and two hours on three evenings a week.

1 At the beginning of the page, the children's facilities at the holiday park are described as tremendous. What word in the next paragraph has a similar meaning to tremendous?

___

2 When a child arrives at the holiday park, what two things is he or she given?

___

3 When parents read that the Club Leaders are experienced, they are likely to be:

surprised	
amused	
reassured	
concerned	

(tick the right answer)

4 Which activity is offered to all three age groups?

___

5 Which of the three clubs is open for the least number of hours per week?

___

6 For each age group, list one activity that is likely to take place outdoors, and one activity that is likely to take place indoors.

___

___

___

___

___

___

___

Not how it seems

Phrases that mean something different from the words used to make them up are called ***idioms.***

Each of these picture clues describes an everyday phrase or saying. Write the phrase or saying in the box beneath each picture. One has been done for you.

Under a cloud means under suspicion. Can you give the real meanings fo the other idioms?

1 under a cloud

2

3

4

5

6

Answers and Hints

In some instances there may be more than one possible answer so you may need to check that the answer your child has given is reasonable. As long as your child's answer makes sense and has shown they understand the question, you should mark it right. Sometimes the question will ask them to fill in facts about themselves, or to express an opinion, or to create their own piece of work. You may want to judge your child's effort for yourself, but please remember that encouragement is always more helpful than criticism.

In the activities that require your child to write something for themselves, they may need your help to get started, and you might find it useful to spend a few minutes discussing how they might go about tackling the task. At school the teacher would make sure that the class or group generated some examples and ideas before beginning to complete the work by themselves.

PAGE 5
1 it's raining 2 I won't do it 3 I'll be seeing you 4 (correct) 5 (correct) 6 you aren't old enough 7 (correct) 8 Where's my coat?

PAGES 6 & 7
Check that your child has correctly identified the ten words beginning with b. You child should have copied them from the top unnumbered grid into alphabetical order in the numbered grid. 1 bag 2 ball 3 balloons 4 bananas 5 bat 6 bicycle 7 books 8 boy 9 bread 10 bucket Check that your child has understood how to use alliteration (their sentences should each use several words with the same beginning sound).

PAGE 8
rhyme pairs (any order): eight–late, sleep–heap, taste–waist, soup–hoop, heart–cart, bite–fight, code–road, term–firm

PAGE 9
across: (1) France, (4) Italy, (5) China, (7) Spain, (9) America, (10) Turkey **down**: (2) Australia, (3) Iceland, (6) India, (7) Sweden, (8) Chile Crosswords encourage children to think about words and their meanings. They can help to increase your child's vocabulary and also serve as an aid to accurate spelling.

PAGES 10 & 11
Comprehension exercises play an important part in the National Tests. Encourage your child to refer back to the passage when answering questions. 1 the mangy Dish-Licker 2 a maker of mischief, a teller of tales and an eater of rags 3 Shere Khan the tiger has moved his hunting grounds and will be hunting in the hills near them 4 Shere Khan 5 a cave with a small entrance

PAGES 12 & 13
Your child needs to understand how a dictionary works. Encourage them to make regular use of one, preferably one designed especially for children. 1 a joey 2 tomatoes 3 a kidnapper 4 a young goat 5 keenness 6 four 7 kilo 8 1000 (one thousand) Check your child's questions – are they about words from the dictionary page?

PAGE 14
Encourage your child to use a wide vocabulary when writing. Said is an example of an overused word – often there are more interesting and more effective alternatives. 1 (missing word) added 2 revealed 3 demanded 4 admitted 5 bellowed 6 began 7 pleaded 8 enquired 9 apologised 10 suggested

PAGE 15
2 (missing word) meet 3 threw 4 is (or am) 5 run 6 climbed 7 think 8 drew 9 wrote 10 hide 11 spun (or span) 12 heard 13 saw 14 had 15 knew 16 were 17 lit

PAGE 16
correct moving words (any order): an eagle swoops, a snake glides, a monkey climbs, a mouse scampers, a cock struts, a bull charges, a tortoise crawls, a horse gallops, a duck waddles

PAGE 17
1 (bottom to top) cool, cold, freezing 2 plain, ugly, hideous 3 edible, tasty, delicious 4 light, bright, dazzling 5 discussion, disagreement, row 6 small, minute, microscopic 7 displeased, angry, outraged 8 nervous, scared, terrified

PAGES 18 & 19
Encourage your child to make use of a thesaurus as well as a dictionary. 1 clump 2 enormous 3 by saluting him 4 land 5 creak 6 six 7 pitch 8 a beam of delight (your child may need to look at definitions in a dictionary to answer this question)

PAGE 20
1 (common nouns) generosity, honesty, ability, hyena, envelope, city 2 (proper nouns) Patricia, Australia 3 (collective nouns) swarm, regiment

PAGE 21
2 (missing letter) w 3 g 4 w 5 g 6 h 7 k 8 h 9 w 10 k 11 g 12 w 13 whole, hole 14 knight, night 15 ringing, wringing 16 right, write

PAGE 22
1 (connected word and definition) practise – to do something regularly… 2 reptile – a cold-blooded animal… 3 delay – to put off until later 4 magnet – an object, such as a piece of iron… 5 repeat – to say or do again 6 pause – to stop for a short time 7 terminate – to bring to an end 8 attract – to draw towards you

PAGE 23
correct group nouns (any order): a band of musicians, a shoal of fish, a fleet of ships, a swarm of bees, a clump of trees, a herd of buffaloes, a choir of singers

PAGE 24
1 (connected saying and meaning) show a clean pair of heels – escape very quickly 2 the apple of one's eye – a person who is cherished… 3 make a clean breast of something – tell the whole truth 4 a wet blanket – a person who's not very encouraging… 5 in the same boat – in a similar situation 6 get into hot water – get into trouble 7 at a loose end – having nothing to do 8 a feather in one's cap – an achievement to be proud of

PAGE 25
correct possessives (any order): Mike's computer, Sasha's mother, Ellena's gift, the girls' sweets, the monkeys' babies, Jake's ball

PAGES 26 & 27
Make sure your child understands that with multiple-choice questions it is important to consider all of the possible answers before deciding which one is correct. 1 (ticked answer) more than five pounds 2 night 3 because the Owl looked up at 'the stars above' 4 the Pussy-Cat's 5 near the sea 6 because the poem tells us they were 'on the edge of the sand' 7 (above) love, (wood) stood, (hill) will, (moon) spoon

PAGE 28
synonym pairs (any order): lean–thin, outside–exterior, weak–feeble, disaster–calamity, care–caution, foe–enemy, annually–yearly, gather–assemble, amount–quantity, vacant–empty

PAGE 29
1 (missing word) before 2 until 3 when 4 unless 5 although 6 or 7 while 8 because 9 after 10 if

PAGES 30 & 31

adverbs (any order): anxiously, eventually, patiently, fondly, visibly, silently, sulkily, clumsily, joyfully, heavily There are lots of possible answers for each verb, so provided your child has written three adverbs that could be used to describe each word you should mark them correct.

PAGE 32

1 (correct word) where 2 wear 3 ate 4 eight 5 night 6 knight 7 new 8 knew 9 whether 10 weather

PAGE 33

opposite pairs: tame–wild, home–abroad, deny–confirm, wealthy–poor, plural–singular, present–absent, superior–inferior, temporary–permanent, separate–join, unite–divide (Your child may have written the last two pairs as separate–divide and unite–join, which you should mark as correct even though separate–join and unite–divide are 'stronger' opposites.)

PAGE 34

1 broom 2 cat 3 heads 4 dogs 5 minds 6 chickens 7 hay 8 haste 9 apple 10 basket

PAGE 35

1 pattern – a regularly repeated arrangement... 2 frost – white powdery ice... 3 monk – one of a group of men... 4 diagram – a drawing that explains something... 5 modem – a small machine that sends information... 6 icicle – a pointed stick of ice... 7 software – programs which control the way a computer works 8 priest – a person trained for various religious duties

PAGES 36 & 37

1 hoisted 2 cloth 3 drizzle, shower, rainstorm 4 mac 5 stick 6 collecting 7 breeds 8 it could mean 'What a noise!' or 'What a tennis racket!'

PAGE 38

2 (missing word) mouse 3 train 4 fair 5 box 6 post 7 fine 8 pupil 9 dear 10 grain

PAGE 39

1 leaves 2 ladder 3 slave 4 shave 5 shady 6 lead 7 bread

PAGES 40 & 41

1 both 2 disapproval 3 three 4 China 5 direction 6 round 7 plastic 8 directions

PAGES 42 & 43

Check that your child knows what syllables are (by year 5 they should have been introduced at school) and understands how they are used in poetry. Read you child's poems and try and help them if they cannot make the words fit easily.

PAGES 44 & 45

1 blaze, inferno 2 (ticked answer) next to 3 thirteen 4 (ticked answer) Soon after Christopher rang the fire brigade the whole restaurant was on fire. 5 (ticked answer) several other shopkeepers are in a similar situation to Marion Murphy 6 (ticked answer) people were made to leave the buildings

PAGE 46

1 (missing words) piece, peace 2 pair, pear 3 aloud, allowed 4 hair, hare 5 tale, tail 6 son, sun 7 fair, fare 8 right, write

PAGE 47

1 (missing word) over 2 beside 3 behind 4 on 5 through 6 between 7 under 8 across

PAGE 48

1 comma – used to mark a pause 2 question mark – used at the end of a sentence that asks something 3 hyphen – a dash that sometimes joins two words... 4 full stop – found at the end of a sentence 5 colon – used to introduce something, such as a list 6 exclamation mark – used to make a point strongly 7 brackets – there are always two of these 8 apostrophe – used to show that part of a word is missing...

PAGE 49

correct spellings (any order): sister, whole, lovely, light, while, meant, because, suddenly, making, caught Encourage your child to proof-read their writing, correcting their own mistakes. Errors are often caused by carelessness or writing too quickly.

PAGE 50

Here are some possible replacements of the word got in these sentences. Your child may have used a different word in some cases; provided the word makes sense and properly replaces the got word, mark it correct. 1 arrived 2 received 3 reached 4 caught 5 bought 6 went 7 scored 8 climbed 9 must 10 has

PAGE 51

2 thought (or thinker) 3 encouragement 4 advertisement 5 action (or actor) 6 movement 7 opposition 8 explanation 9 accidental 10 careful 11 foolish 12 beautiful 13 patient 14 strong 15 anxious 16 comfortable

PAGE 52

1 (correct) 2 there's a policeman 3 Elizabeth's diary 4 ladies' shoes 5 (correct) 6 I can't see it 7 it's a nice day 8 (correct) 9 (correct) 10 (correct)

PAGE 53

1 (correct word) is 2 saw 3 Have 4 were 5 is 6 was 7 was 8 Weren't 9 are 10 has

PAGES 54 & 55

Check that your child has included only the essential instructions – you may need to discuss what these are before your child attempts the activity.

PAGE 56

words: handcuffs, heart, handlebars, harp, hill, hen, hedge, headband 1 handcuffs 2 handlebars 3 harp 4 headband 5 heart 6 hedge 7 hen 8 hill

PAGE 57

correct spellings (any order): shivered, distance, playground, dreading, captain, really, protest, shouted, passed ('...he had passed all but one...'), through

PAGE 58

There are lots of possible answers to this activity. Check your child's suggestions; provided they have written a more powerful word mark it correct. (Example answers (in order): exhausted, hilarious, gigantic, brilliant, destroyed, terrified, filthy, ancient, ugly, miserable, starving, drenched.)

PAGE 59

There are lots of possible answers. Check your child's suggestions; provided they have written a sensible replacement word mark it correct. (Example answers (in order): chuckled, whispered, shouted, announced, growled, moaned, gasped, shrieked, sneered.)

PAGES 60 & 61

1 terrific 2 a Fun Pack and a Season Ticket 3 (ticked answer) reassured 4 video sessions 5 Littluns 6 (possible answers) (outdoor, Littluns) butterfly hunts, teddy bear's picnics; (outdoor, Middluns) mini Olympics, wacky races, treasure hunts; (outdoor, Biguns) beach volleyball; (indoor, Littuns) bedtime stories, face painting, video sessions; (indoor, Middluns) postcard designing, fancy dress, face painting, video sessions; (indoor, Biguns) discos, talent shows, video sessions

PAGE 62

2 over the moon (means to be extremely delighted about something) 3 to pull someone's leg (means to tease them) 4 to put the cart before the horse (means to reverse the right or natural order of things) 5 to smell a rat (means to be suspicious, sense something is not right) 6 raining cats and dogs (means to rain very heavily)